SNOW WHITE
and the THREE GIANTS

One afternoon, on her way to visit the Dwarfs, Snow White was so busy talking with her friends that she accidentally took the wrong path.

The path led to a cottage, but it didn't look very familiar.

When Snow White peeked inside, she was surprised to see
three immense chairs instead of seven little ones.

There was no sign of the tiny kitchen where she loved to cook. Instead an enormous hearth held a huge, crackling fire.

The dining room table was as big as a barn! Suddenly, the ground began to tremble.

"What's happening?" cried Snow White.

STOMP! STOMP! STOMP! The three largest people Snow White had ever seen entered the cottage.

They were heading for the table. Snow White felt
nervous, but she knew what she had to do.

She stepped out from behind the table and said, "Pardon me, gentlemen."

"Ahh!" cried one giant, knocking over his chair, while the other two stared at her in surprise.

"Where did you come from?" asked the tallest giant. "We haven't had a visitor in ages!"

"Won't you stay for supper?" the smallest giant smiled encouragingly.

The giants brought cushions for her seat so she could reach the top of the table. They found her a tiny plate, a thimble for a cup, and even a miniature napkin.

They ate and talked and laughed together.
After dinner, Snow White even sang them a song.

The next time
Snow White saw the
Dwarfs she told them
about the giants.

"I'd be too shy to talk to a giant!" said Bashful.

"Don't they breathe fire?" asked Dopey.

"Of course not," answered Snow White. "They are perfectly
sweet and kind!"

"Never trust tall people!" Grumpy exclaimed.

Snow White laughed. "Oh Grumpy, does that mean you don't trust me? Because you can! Just wait and see. I think we're all going to get along just fine!"

Snow White decided to have a party. She sent out invitations and planned the menu. Now she just needed a good party game to help everyone get to know each other!

On the day of the party, Snow White waited until all of her guests had arrived. Then she announced her plan. "Let's play a game called Ditto! Everyone will take a turn to say one thing about themselves, and if it's true about you, too, shout 'Ditto'! I'll start."

Snow White smiled. "I have two eyes with which to see the world!"

"DITTO!" boomed the giants.
"DITTO!" bellowed the Dwarfs.

"You go next, Bashful!" said Snow White.

"Well," said Bashful, blushing, "I have two ears that love to listen to Snow White singing!"

"DITTO!" thundered the giants.
"DITTO!" roared the Dwarfs.

The largest giant was next. "I have one nose, and with it I can smell a delicious dinner!"

"DITTO!" yelled the giants.

"DITTO!" shouted the Dwarfs. It turned out that they all had hungry bellies in common, too.

By the end of the meal they were all fast friends. "I had a great time tonight," said the smallest giant. Everyone answered, "DITTO!"